BEAR'S HOME

Find and colour...

- BEAR decorating his den with beautiful flowers from the woodland
- WEASEL poking her head out of a log
- MAMA WREN and PAPA WREN gathering sticks to build their nest
- SPIDER spinning heart shapes
- A FOX CUB who has gone wandering

- FROG dusting his home
- ANT climbing a staircase
- GRANDMA BAT and GRANDPA BAT roosting upside-down
- RACCOON'S leaf-lined bed
- MOUSE riding piggyback

- Two BUNNIES with brooms
- PAPA BEAR collecting flowers
- Four NESTS full of eggs
- FAWNS watering some bluebells
- RED ADMIRAL BUTTERFLY on MAMA DEER'S velvety nose

BEAR'S SCHOOL

Find and colour...

- BEAR reciting poetry to his classmates
- MAMA SQUIRREL teaching the animals how to count
- PROFESSOR OWL giving a lesson on the moon
- A lively game of HOPSCOTCH
- SPARROW leading a chirping, cheeping choir
- SPIDER teaching the alphabet
- Three CATERPILLARS looking at leaves *very* closely
- A NEW STUDENT, here for the summer months, being made welcome
- A WOODLAND MAP
- FROG teaching a science lesson on a lily pad
- A SKIPPING game
- Two BOATS on the pond
- PAPA RACCOON teaching a lesson on fungi
- MAMA MOUSE waving goodbye
- A PACKED LUNCH

BEAR'S SPECIAL FRIEND

Find and colour...

- ○ **BEAR** and his friends measuring Grand Old Oak's trunk
- ○ **BUNNY** counting the growth rings on a tree stump
- ○ Two **SKUNKS** wearing pyjamas
- ○ **PAPA MOUSE** reading aloud
- ○ Two **WIND CHIMES**
- ○ A ringing **ALARM CLOCK**
- ○ **MAMA PIGEON** and **PAPA PIGEON** with their beaks full of twigs
- ○ **MAMA DEER** with a tape measure
- ○ A **MORNING STAR**
- ○ Baby **CHIPMUNKS** brushing their teeth
- ○ **FROG** having a big stretch
- ○ **PROFESSOR OWL** heading for bed
- ○ **BEAR'S LITTLE BROTHER** and **SISTER** learning how to tell the time
- ○ Two cosy **NESTS**
- ○ **SQUIRREL** pouring tea

PLANNING A PARTY

Find and colour...

- BEAR sharing his ideas to celebrate Bunny's birthday
- BUNNY hopping with happiness
- PAPA MOUSE starting a to-do list
- Half of MAMA WEASEL
- Three PICNIC HAMPERS
- BEAR'S LITTLE BROTHER and SISTER throwing leaf confetti
- MAMA FOX with two baskets of foraged leaves and berries
- Half of SNAKE
- Fourteen stripy BEES
- The FOX CUBS falling over in excitement
- SPIDER weaving an oak-leaf web
- A choir of BIRDS singing with joy
- NANA RABBIT and PAPA BEAR looking through a birthday cake recipe book
- FROG perched on a mushroom
- Two CUPCAKES

BUNNY'S BIRTHDAY

Find and colour...

- **BEAR** hiding behind a curtain with a trio of mice
- **BUNNY** wearing his birthday crown
- **SNAKE** slithering to the party, with a basket
- A pile of **PRESENTS** and **CARDS**
- Three **BUTTERFLIES**, pretty as a picture
- **MAMA RABBIT** welcoming guests
- A **HATFUL** of Bunny's brothers and sisters
- **NANA RABBIT** putting the finishing touches on the birthday cake
- Ten **BALLOONS**
- A game of **PIN-THE-TAIL**
- Three topsy-turvy **SNAILS**
- Two **BABY WEASELS** wriggling into wellies
- A plate of wibbly-wobbly **JELLY**
- **PAPA RABBIT** pinning up bunting
- Three **BUNNIES** hiding under the table

SWIMMING LESSON

Find and colour...

- ○ **BEAR** drying off after his swim
- ○ A shy **FROG**
- ○ A **SHOAL** of **FISH**
- ○ **PROFESSOR OWL** and **RACCOON** watching over the swimmers
- ○ **MOUSE** dipping her toe into the water

- ○ **FOX CUBS** playing chase
- ○ **BEAR'S LITTLE BROTHER, BEAR'S LITTLE SISTER** and the **FAWNS** making waves
- ○ **GRANDPA TOAD** watching over his grandchildren
- ○ **MAMA FOX** and **MAMA DEER** drinking the swimming pool
- ○ **MAMA WEASEL'S** book club

- ○ **PAPA BEAR** and **PAPA DEER** enjoying a thermos of tea
- ○ **MAMA RABBIT** in a captain's hat
- ○ Five surfing **MICE**
- ○ A **TREE HOUSE**
- ○ A game of **CATCH**

SUMMER PICNIC

Find and colour...

- BEAR eating a bowl of WILD STRAWBERRIES

- MICE and CHIPMUNKS playing catch

- SWIMMING COSTUMES drying on a mossy log

- A FOX CUB swinging her bat

- NANA RABBIT under a sunshade

- MAMA DEER helping the others stay cool

- Twelve different HATS

- A basket of BREAD

- A WHISKERY NOSE poking out of a book

- A speedy PICNIC BASKET

- A HANDSTAND and a CARTWHEEL

- Three friends making DAISY CHAINS

- Two pots of TEA

- A platter of CHEESE

- BUNNY enjoying a cold, refreshing ice cream

- A tiny DOOR

- MOUSE smelling honeysuckle

BEAR HELPS WITH A PLAY

Find and colour...

- ○ **BEAR** and **WEASEL** helping the stars to twinkle
- ○ A **FAIRY KING** and **FAIRY QUEEN** wearing handmade crowns
- ○ **GRANDPA TOAD** making tickets, with a little help from his friends
- ○ **MAMA FOX** and **MAMA WEASEL** painting
- ○ A not-very-fierce **LION**

- ○ Two **BUNNIES** teetering on stilts
- ○ A crescent **MOON**
- ○ **NANA RABBIT** and **PAPA RACCOON** making costumes
- ○ A **FOX CUB** with a bottle of magic potion
- ○ **MAMA MOUSE** directing the play from a great height

- ○ A **GRIN** and a **FROWN**
- ○ **PROFESSOR OWL** decorating the theatre
- ○ **MAMA SQUIRREL** and **PAPA MOUSE** offering refreshments to cast and crew
- ○ **PAPA BEAR** wearing donkey's ears
- ○ **SQUIRREL** doing a handstand

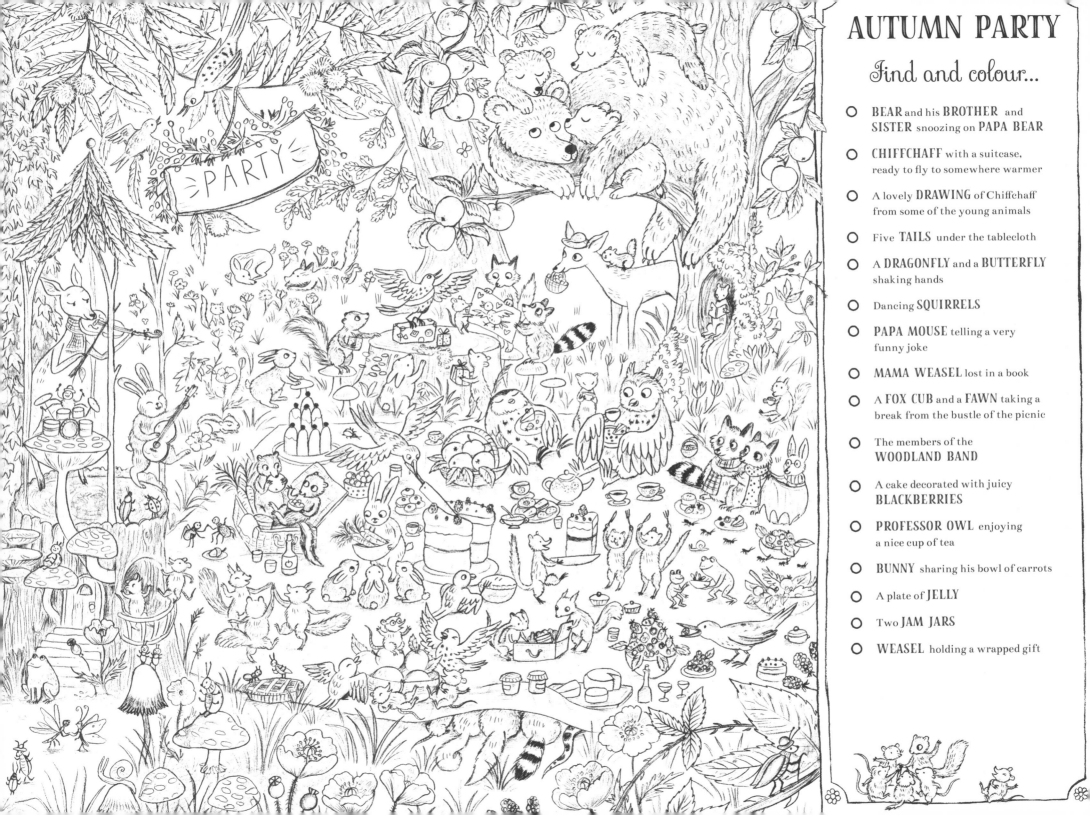

AUTUMN PARTY

Find and colour...

- BEAR and his BROTHER and SISTER snoozing on PAPA BEAR
- CHIFFCHAFF with a suitcase, ready to fly to somewhere warmer
- A lovely DRAWING of Chiffchaff from some of the young animals
- Five TAILS under the tablecloth
- A DRAGONFLY and a BUTTERFLY shaking hands
- Dancing SQUIRRELS
- PAPA MOUSE telling a very funny joke
- MAMA WEASEL lost in a book
- A FOX CUB and a FAWN taking a break from the bustle of the picnic
- The members of the WOODLAND BAND
- A cake decorated with juicy BLACKBERRIES
- PROFESSOR OWL enjoying a nice cup of tea
- BUNNY sharing his bowl of carrots
- A plate of JELLY
- Two JAM JARS
- WEASEL holding a wrapped gift

ART CLASS

Find and colour...

- ○ **BEAR** dreaming up ideas for his next piece of art
- ○ **RED ADMIRAL BUTTERFLY** being a model for the day
- ○ A bowl of **FRUIT** and **NUTS**
- ○ **FOX CUBS** painting a picture with their paws
- ○ **NANA RABBIT** admiring **BUNNY'S** drawing
- ○ **BEAR'S LITTLE SISTER** preparing to start again
- ○ A sculpture made of **TWIGS**
- ○ **RACCOON** crafting a special jug
- ○ **MICE** with needles and thread
- ○ **FROG** painting a vase of flowers
- ○ **SKUNK** being splashed with paint
- ○ The **DEER FAMILY** posing for a portrait
- ○ **SPIDER** holding three paint brushes
- ○ **SQUIRRELS** collecting acorns for their art project
- ○ A mobile made of **FLOWERS**
- ○ An upside-down **ARTIST**
- ○ **SNAIL** way up high

COLLECTING THE MAIL

Find and colour...

- **BEAR** collecting today's post
- **BUNNY** with a pile of important letters and cards
- Two **MILLIPEDES** munching on dead leaves
- **MAMA PIGEON** perched on a tired Grand Old Oak
- A **FALLEN BRANCH**
- **FOX CUB** and **FROG** sorting yesterday's post
- Two yummy **APPLES**
- **MAMA RABBIT** asleep in her chair
- **MOLE** digging a tunnel
- Four wriggling **EARTHWORMS**
- **SNAKE** keeping cosy in a pile of leaves
- **SLUGS** and **WOODLICE** queuing to post letters
- A miniature **OAK TREE**
- Three **MOLEHILLS**
- A **GLOBE**
- **FOX**, **MOLE** and **SPIDER** dancing to music

CRAFT CLUB

Find and colour...

- BEAR making a paper collage
- MOUSE and CHIPMUNK sewing bunting
- BUNNY painting a picture
- MAMA RABBIT and PAPA RABBIT making a banner
- SKUNKS arranging dried leaves and flowers
- BEAR'S LITTLE BROTHER and SISTER stirring fruit cake batter
- BABY WEASELS writing a story
- PAPA BEAR carrying boxes of craft supplies
- The FAWNS keeping everyone hydrated
- PAPA MOUSE handing out refreshments
- Four mugs of HOT CHOCOLATE
- A decorated PAPA DEER
- PROFESSOR OWL composing a poem
- The WOODLAND BAND rehearsing
- Two WHEELBARROWS full of lovely things
- A sleeping FOX CUB

RAINY DAY

Find and colour...

- BEAR catching a leak
- An upside-down NEST being used for shelter
- BEETLES with leafy umbrellas
- PAPA SKUNK snoozing in a tree
- FROG, TOAD and MICE jumping into puddles
- BUNNIES having a water fight
- WEASELS and RACCOON making mud pies
- SNAKE, BEAR'S LITTLE BROTHER and BAT gazing at raindrops
- MAMA WOODPECKER and PROFESSOR OWL enjoying a hot chocolate
- Seven SNAILS enjoying the rain
- NANA RABBIT reading her book
- One of the FAWNS munching an apple
- MAMA WEASEL despairing over a very muddy BABY WEASEL
- A wet WASHING LINE
- A BABY MOUSE wearing a raincoat

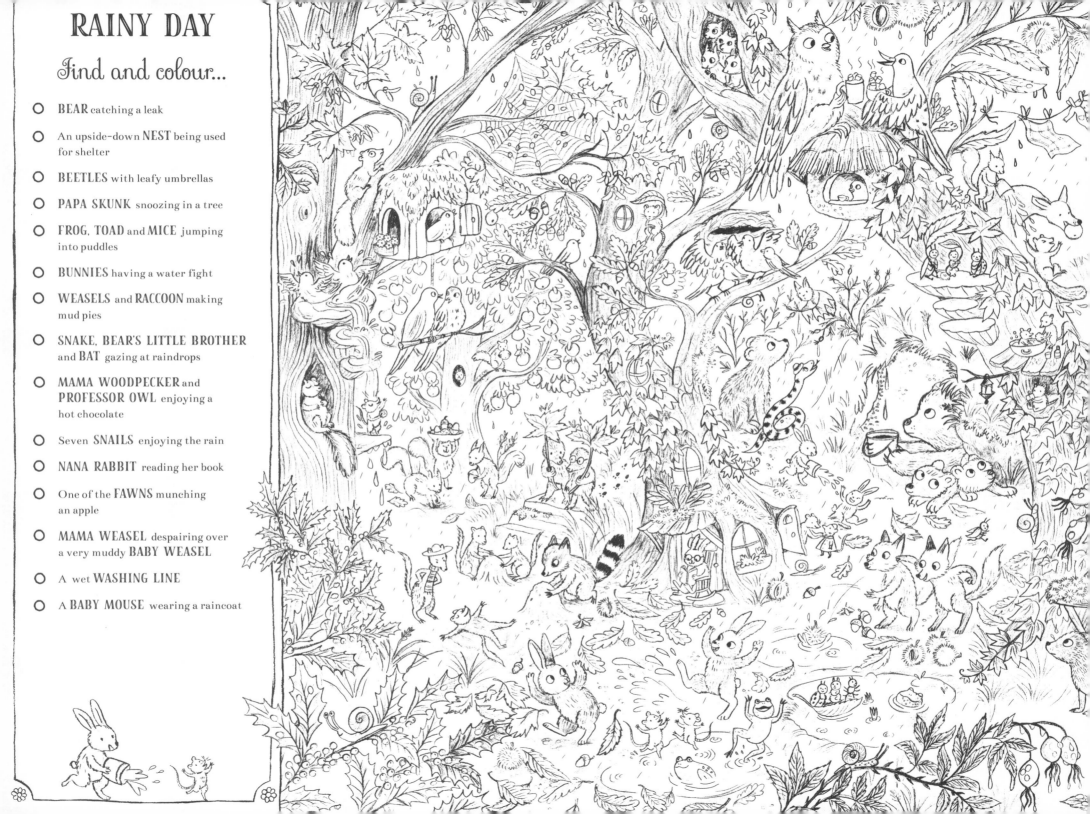

WINTER FEAST

Find and colour...

- BEAR wearing a leaf and berry crown
- A MAP of the woods
- Three MICE performing in special costumes
- BUNNY, FAWN and a FOX CUB making garlands
- RACCOONS welcoming guests to the feast

- A game of DOMINOS
- PAPA DEER'S decorated antlers
- A nearly completed JIGSAW PUZZLE
- A PUPPET THEATRE show
- A book of SONGS

- CHIPMUNK perching on a pie
- ANTS doing a line dance
- A very hungry SKUNK
- The winter SUN low in the sky
- The SQUIRREL FAMILY being generous with their acorns

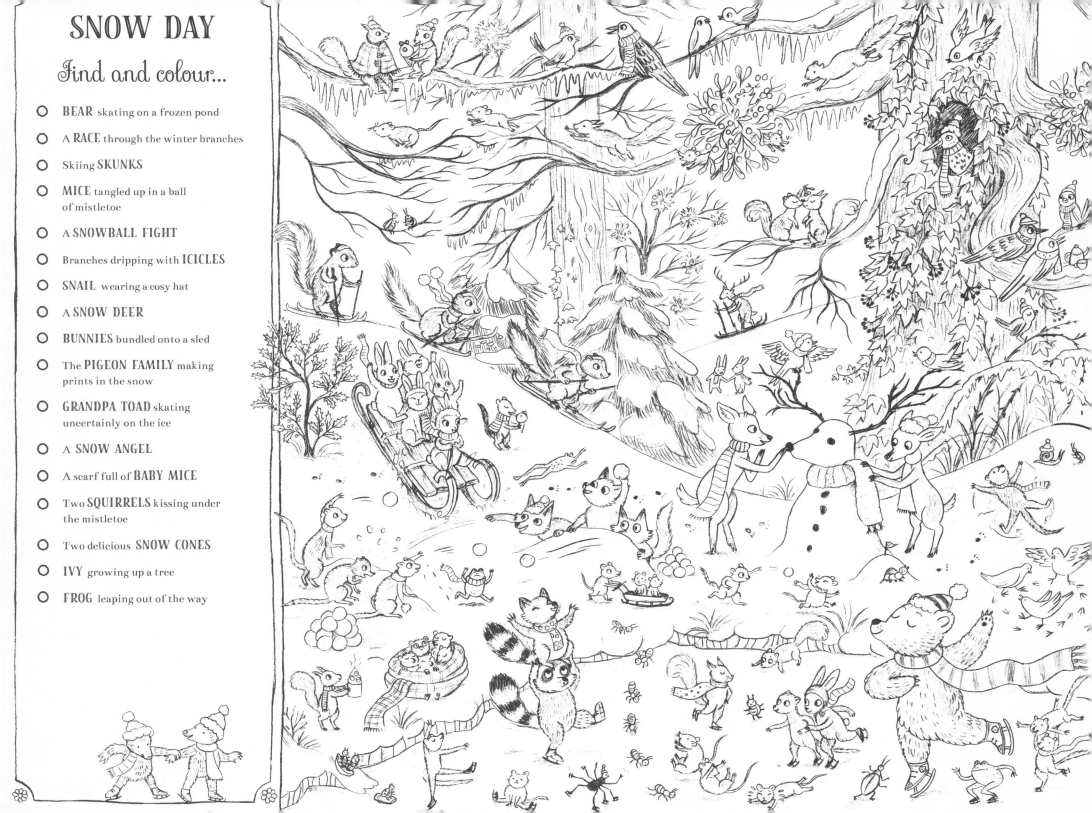

SNOW DAY

Find and colour...

- BEAR skating on a frozen pond
- A RACE through the winter branches
- Skiing SKUNKS
- MICE tangled up in a ball of mistletoe
- A SNOWBALL FIGHT
- Branches dripping with ICICLES
- SNAIL wearing a cosy hat
- A SNOW DEER
- BUNNIES bundled onto a sled
- The PIGEON FAMILY making prints in the snow
- GRANDPA TOAD skating uncertainly on the ice
- A SNOW ANGEL
- A scarf full of BABY MICE
- Two SQUIRRELS kissing under the mistletoe
- Two delicious SNOW CONES
- IVY growing up a tree
- FROG leaping out of the way

BEAR PERFORMS IN A PLAY

Find and colour...

- BEAR on centre stage
- An ACORN, CATKIN and BUTTERFLY ballet
- PROFESSOR OWL dressed as a famous writer
- Twelve glowing LANTERNS
- Two OAK BARRELS with bushy tails
- A pot of INK made from acorns and a FEATHER QUILL
- A sign showing some of the 2,300 SPECIES supported by oak trees
- A sphere of MISTLETOE with berries
- A walking loaf of BREAD made from acorn flour
- Three homemade LIGHTNING BOLTS
- The WOODLAND BAND playing music
- MAMA RACCOON cleverly juggling acorns
- A BOAT made of oak
- A wheelbarrow piled high with ACORNS
- Six STARS